EASIEST KEYBOARD COLLECTION

Karaoke Classics

WISE PUBLICATIONS
part of The Music Sales Group
London/New York/Paris/Sydney/Copenhagen/Berlin/Madrid/Tokyo

Published by
Wise Publications
14-15 Berners Street,
London W1T 3LJ, UK.

Exclusive Distributors:
Music Sales Limited
Distribution Centre, Newmarket Road,
Bury St Edmunds, Suffolk, IP33 3YB, UK.
Music Sales Pty Limited
120 Rothschild Avenue,
Rosebery, NSW 2018,
Australia.

Order No. AM985072
ISBN 1-84609-458-5
This book © Copyright 2006 by Wise Publications
a division of Music Sales Limited.

Compiled by Nick Crispin.
Music arranged by Derek Jones.
Music processed by Paul Ewers Music Design.

Printed in the EU.

Your Guarantee of Quality
As publishers, we strive to produce every book to the highest
commercial standards.
The music has been freshly engraved and the book has been carefully
designed to minimise awkward page turns and to make playing from
it a real pleasure.
Particular care has been given to specifying acid-free, neutral-sized
paper made from pulps which have not been elemental chlorine
bleached. This pulp is from farmed sustainable forests and was
produced with special regard for the environment.
Throughout, the printing and binding have been planned to ensure
a sturdy, attractive publication which should give years of enjoyment.
If your copy fails to meet our high standards, please inform us and
we will gladly replace it.

www.musicsales.com

Contents

ANGELS

Words & Music by Robbie Williams & Guy Chambers

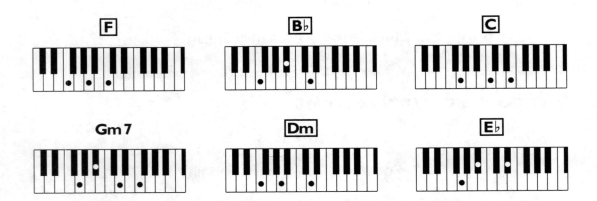

Voice: **Studio Piano**

Rhythm: **Pop Ballad**

Tempo: ♩ = 74

I sit and wait, does an an - gel con - tem - plate—

— my fate?— And do they know the pla - ces where we

go when we're grey and old?—— 'Cos I have been—

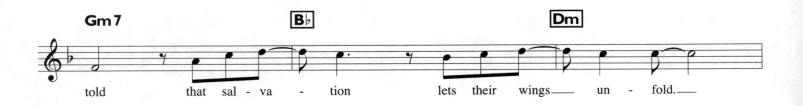

told that sal - va - tion lets their wings— un - fold.—

So when I'm ly-ing in my bed, thoughts run-ning through my head and I feel that love is dead,

I'm lov-ing an-gels in-stead. And through it all

she of-fers me pro-tec-tion, a lot of love and af-

-fec-tion, whe-ther I'm right or wrong. And down the wa-ter-fall, wher-ev-er it may

take me, I know that life won't break me, when I come to call, she won't for-

-sake me, I'm lov-ing an-gels in-stead.

BABY ONE MORE TIME

Words & Music by Max Martin

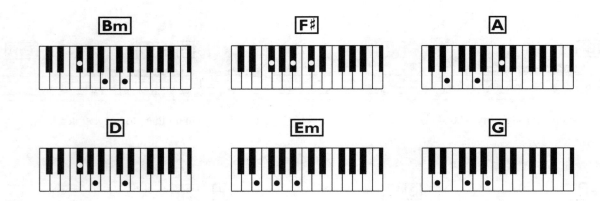

Voice:	**Alto Saxophone**
Rhythm:	**Straight Rock**
Tempo:	♩ = 80

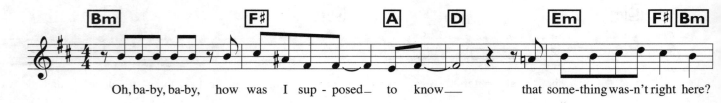

Oh, ba-by, ba-by, how was I sup-posed to know that some-thing was-n't right here?

Oh, ba-by, ba-by, I should-n't have let you go. And now you're out of sight, yeah,

show me how you want it to be. Tell me ba-by 'cos I need to know now, oh, be-cause

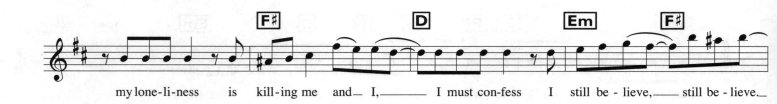

my lone-li-ness is kill-ing me and I, I must con-fess I still be-lieve, still be-lieve.

When I'm not with you I lose my mind, give me a sign,——— hit me, ba - by, one more time.

Oh, ba - by, ba - by, how was I sup - posed——— to know?———

Oh, pret - ty ba - by I should-n't have let——— you go.——— I must con - fess—

——— that my lone - li - ness——— is kill - ing me now.——— Don't you know I——— still——— be - lieve—

——— that you will be here——— and give me a sign.——— Hit me, ba - by, one more time.

My lone - li - ness is kill - ing me and— I,——— I must con - fess I still be - lieve,——— still be - lieve.

Repeat to fade

——— When I'm not with you I lose my mind, give me a sign,——— Hit me, ba - by, one more time.

THE BEST

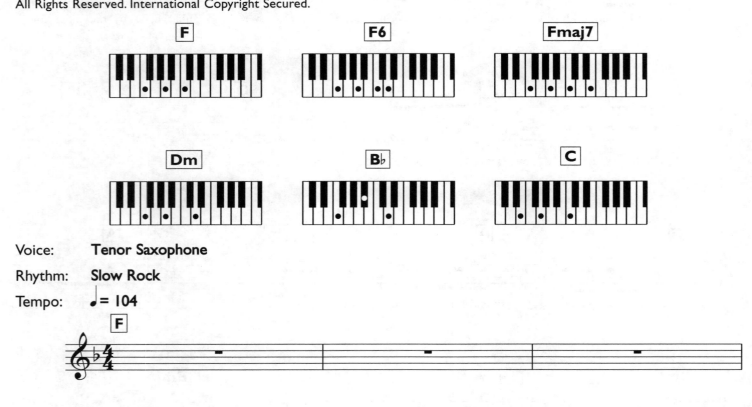

Voice: **Tenor Saxophone**

Rhythm: **Slow Rock**

Tempo: ♩ = 104

I call you when I need you, my heart's on fire.

You come to me, come to me,

wild and wired. Oh, you come to

CAN'T GET YOU OUT OF MY HEAD

Words & Music by Cathy Dennis & Rob Davis

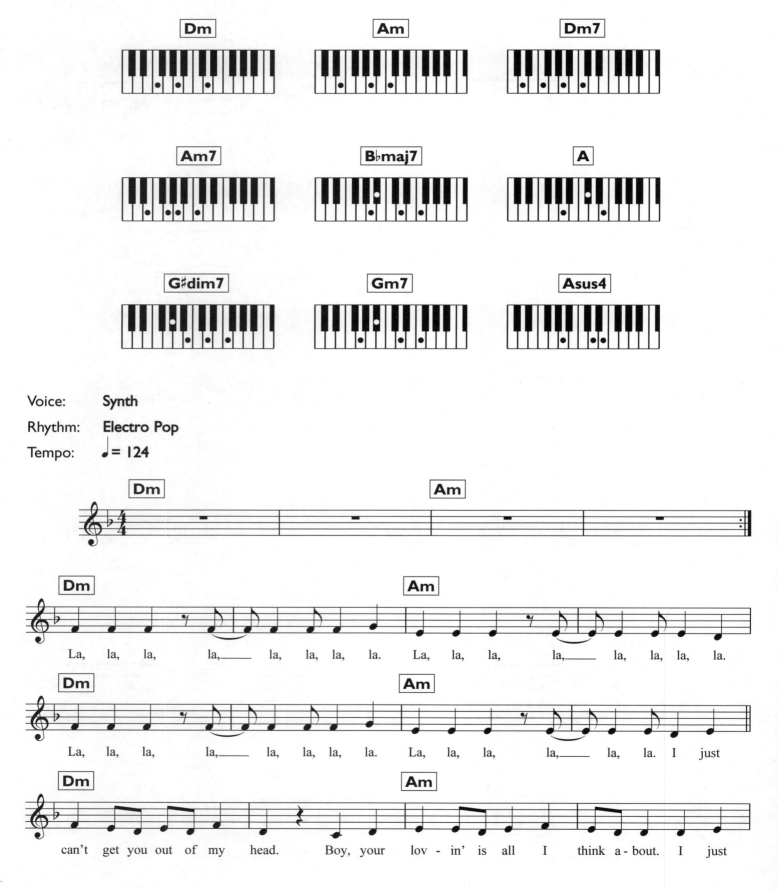

Voice: **Synth**

Rhythm: **Electro Pop**

Tempo: ♩ = 124

La, la, la, la, la, la, la, la. La, la, la, la, la, la, la, la.

La, la, la, la, la, la, la, la. La, la, la, la, la, la. I just

can't get you out of my head. Boy, your lov-in' is all I think a-bout. I just

CRAZY

Words & Music by Willie Nelson

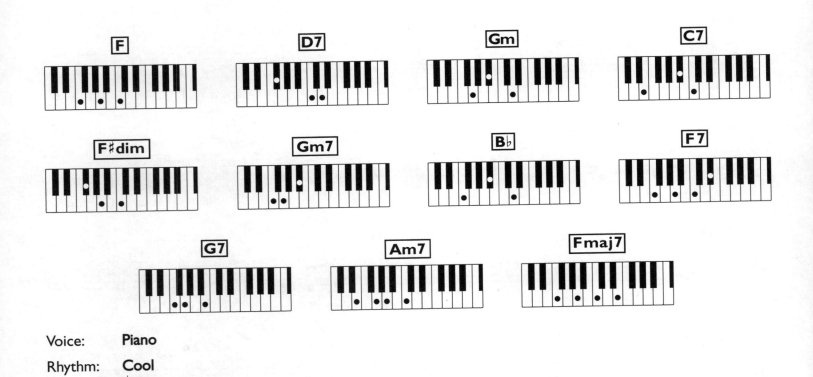

Voice: **Piano**

Rhythm: **Cool**

Tempo: ♩ = 80

Cra - zy,_____ cra - zy for feel - in' so

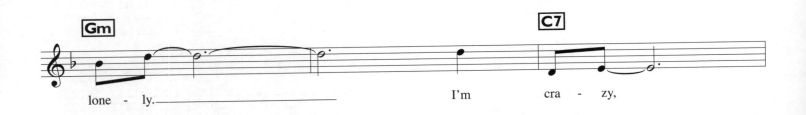

lone - ly._____ I'm cra - zy,

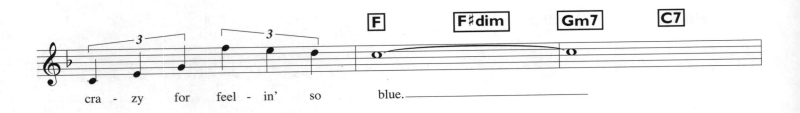

cra - zy for feel - in' so blue._____

FOOTLOOSE

Words & Music by Kenny Loggins & Dean Pitchford

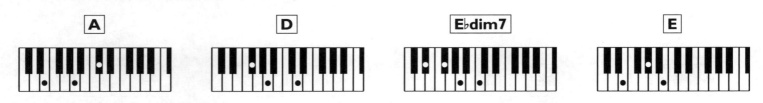

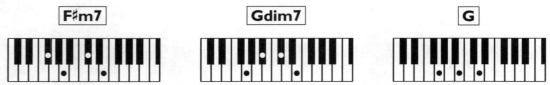

Voice: **Alto Saxophone**

Rhythm: **Straight Rock**

Tempo: ♩ = 190

I been work-ing so hard. I'm punch-ing my card.

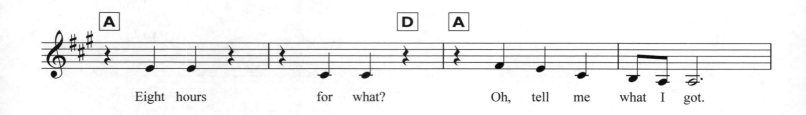

Eight hours for what? Oh, tell me what I got.

I've got this feel-ing that time's just hold-ing me down.

GIRLS JUST WANT TO HAVE FUN

Words & Music by Robert Hazard

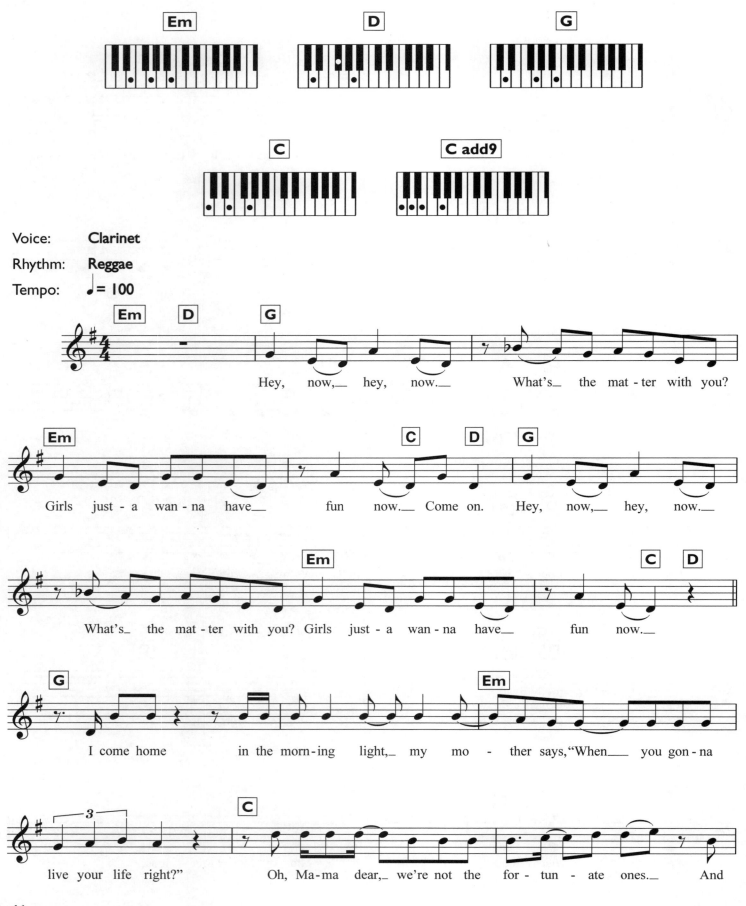

HERO

Words & Music by Enrique Iglesias, Paul Barry & Mark Taylor

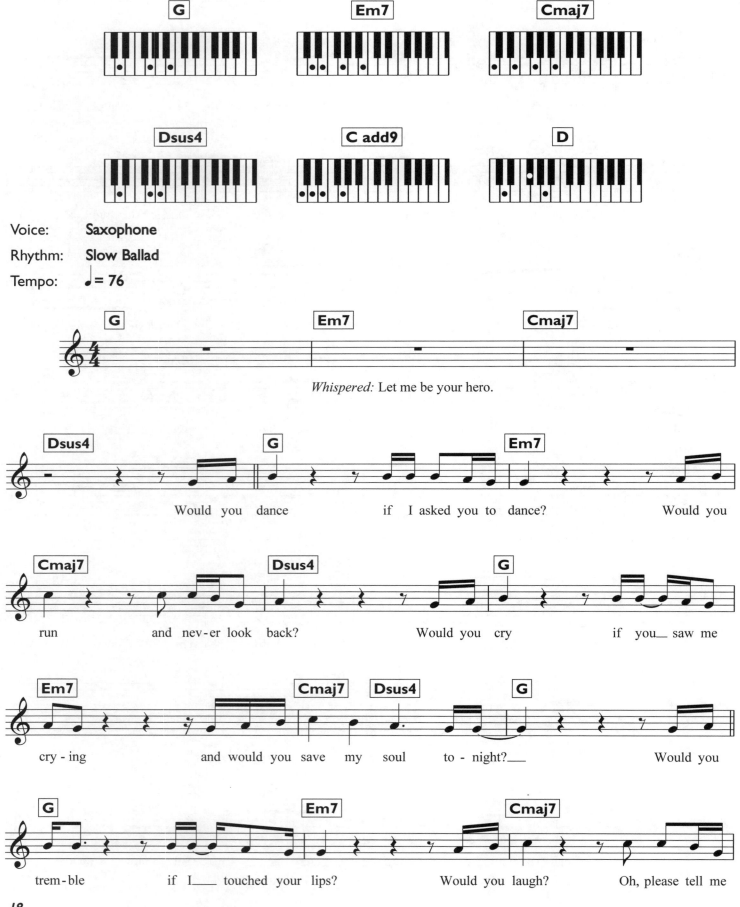

Voice: **Saxophone**

Rhythm: **Slow Ballad**

Tempo: ♩ = 76

Whispered: Let me be your hero.

Would you dance if I asked you to dance? Would you run and nev-er look back? Would you cry if you__ saw me cry-ing and would you save my soul to-night?__ Would you trem-ble if I__ touched your lips? Would you laugh? Oh, please tell me

HEY YA!

Words & Music by André Benjamin

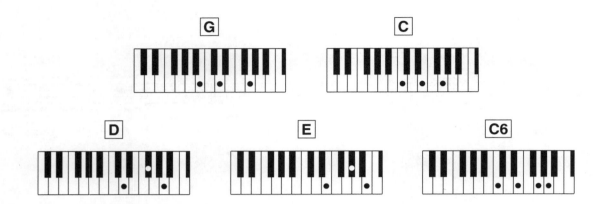

Voice: **Clarinet**

Rhythm: **Pop Rock**

Tempo: ♩ = 144

My ba-by don't mess a-round_ be-cause she loves me so___ and this I

know for sure._____ But does she

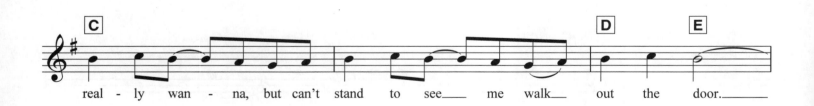

real-ly wan-na, but can't stand to see___ me walk out the door.___

___ Don't try to fight the feel-in' 'cos the

thought a - lone___ is kill - ing me right now.___

Thank God for Mum and Dad___ for stick - ing

two to - ge - ther 'cos we don't know how.___

Hey, ya,_____ hey, ya!_____

Hey, ya,_____ hey ya!_____

Hey, ya,_____ hey, ya!_____

Hey, ya,_____ hey, ya!_____

I WILL SURVIVE

Words & Music by Dino Fekaris & Freddie Perren

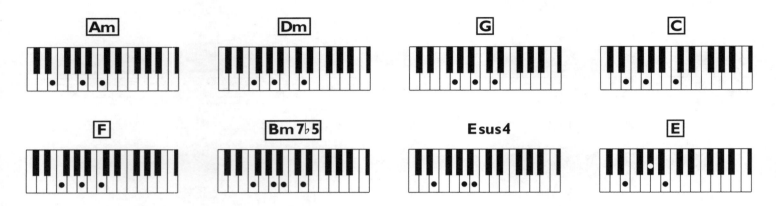

Voice: **Trumpet**

Rhythm: **Disco**

Tempo: ♩= 116

At first I was a-fraid, I was pet-ri-fied,_____ kept think-ing

I could nev-er live with-out you by my side. But then I spent so ma-ny nights think-ing

how you did me wrong and I grew strong, and I learned how to get a-long, and so you're

back from out-er space, I just walked in to find you here with that sad look up-on your face. I should have

changed that stu-pid lock, I should have made you leave your key, if I'd have known for just one sec-ond you'd be

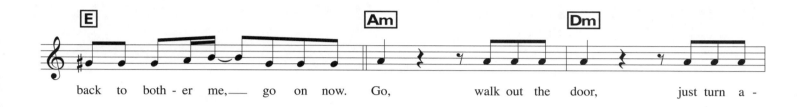

back to both-er me,— go on now. Go, walk out the door, just turn a-

-round now 'cos you're not wel-come a - ny more. Weren't you the one who tried to

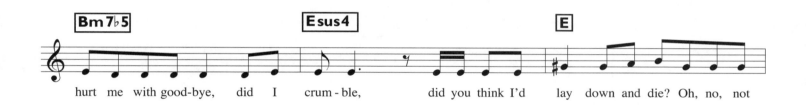

hurt me with good-bye, did I crum-ble, did you think I'd lay down and die? Oh, no, not

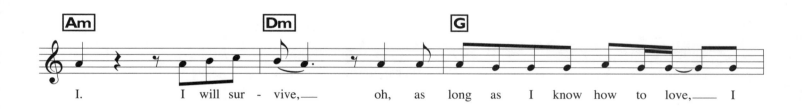

I. I will sur - vive,— oh, as long as I know how to love,— I

know I'll stay a - live. I've got all my life to live, I've got all my love to give and I'll sur -

-vive, I will sur - vive, I'll sur - vive.—

I'M A BELIEVER

Words & Music by Neil Diamond
© Copyright 1966 Stonebridge Music Incorporated/
Colgems-EMI Music Incorporated, USA.
Sony/ATV Music Publishing (UK) Limited (75%)/
Screen Gems-EMI Music Limited (25%).
All Rights Reserved. International Copyright Secured.

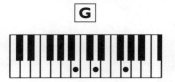 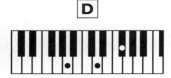 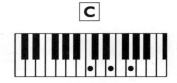 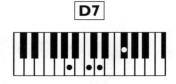

 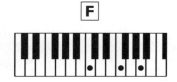 

Voice: Rock Organ

Rhythm: Lite Pop

Tempo: ♩ = 150

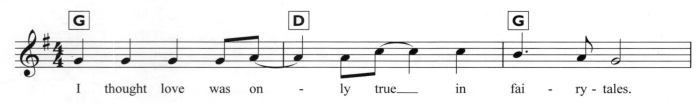

I thought love was on - ly true____ in fai - ry - tales.

Meant for some - one else____ but not for

me. Oh, love was out to get____

____ me. That's the way it seemed.____

Dis - ap - point - ment haunt - ed all my dreams._____

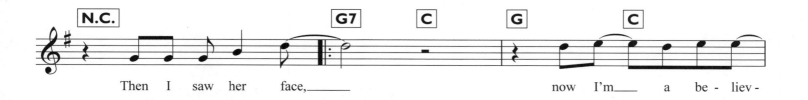

Then I saw her face,_____ now I'm_____ a be - liev -

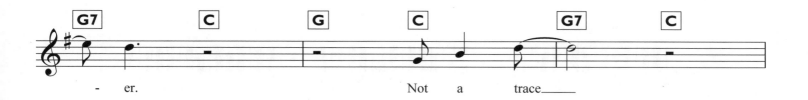

- er. Not a trace_____

of doubt_____ in my mind. I'm in

love, I'm_____ a be - liev - er, I could - n't

Repeat to fade

leave her if I tried._____ Yes, I saw her face,_

(I'VE HAD) THE TIME OF MY LIFE

Words & Music by Frankie Previte, John DeNicola & Donald Markowitz

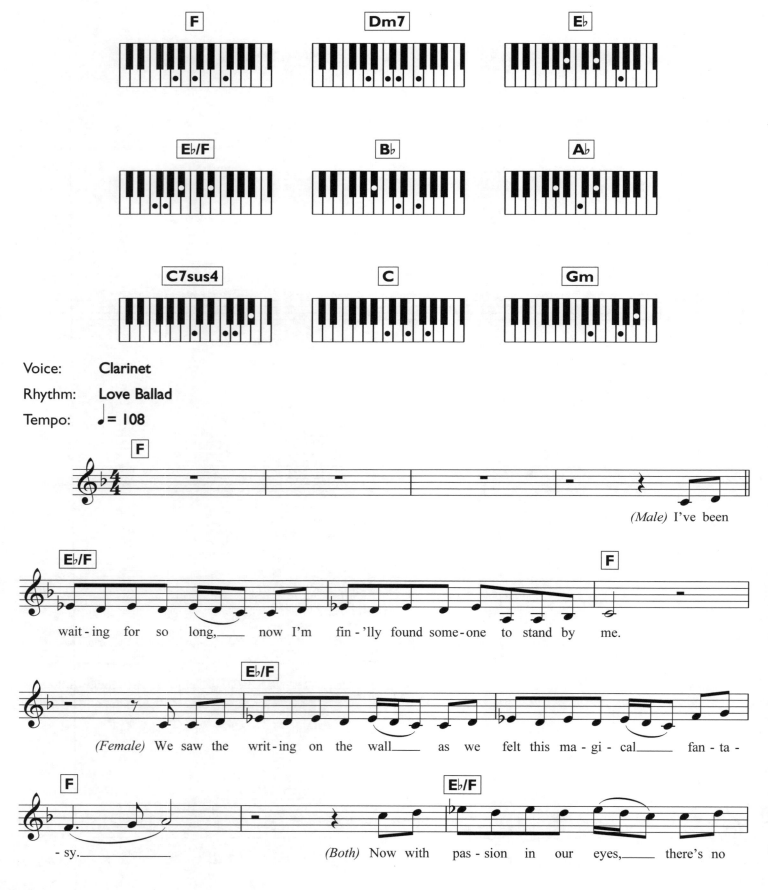

LIKE A PRAYER

Words & Music by Madonna & Pat Leonard

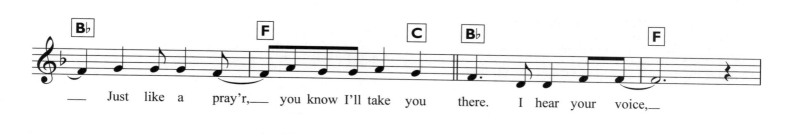

Just like a pray'r,— you know I'll take you there. I hear your voice,—

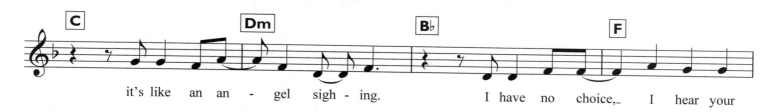

it's like an an - gel sigh - ing. I have no choice,— I hear your

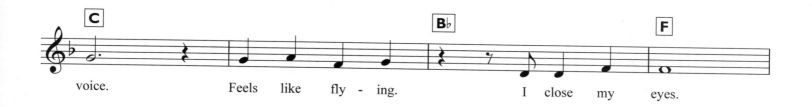

voice. Feels like fly - ing. I close my eyes.

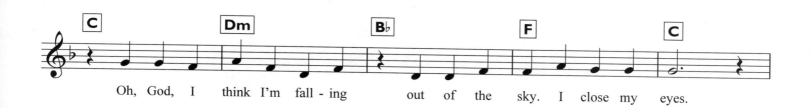

Oh, God, I think I'm fall - ing out of the sky. I close my eyes.

Hea - ven help me. (there.) When you call my name— it's like a lit - tle pray'r,—

— I'm down on my knees,— I wan - na take you there. In the mid - night hour—

Repeat to fade

— I can feel your pow'r.— Just like a pray'r,— you know I'll take you

MAN! I FEEL LIKE A WOMAN

Words & Music by Shania Twain & R.J. Lange

MY WAY

Words & Music by Claude Francois, Jacques Revaux & Gilles Thibaut

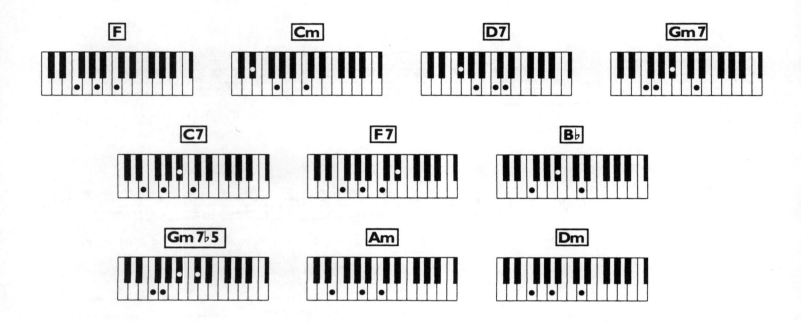

Voice: **Harp**

Rhythm: **Epic Ballad**

Tempo: ♩ = 98

And now _____ the end is near _____ and so I

face _____ the fi - nal cur - tain. _____ My friend, _____ I'll say it

clear, _____ I'll state my case _____ of which I'm cer - tain. _____ I've

NOTHING COMPARES 2 U

Words & Music by Prince
© Copyright 1985 Controversy Music, USA.
Universal/MCA Music Limited.

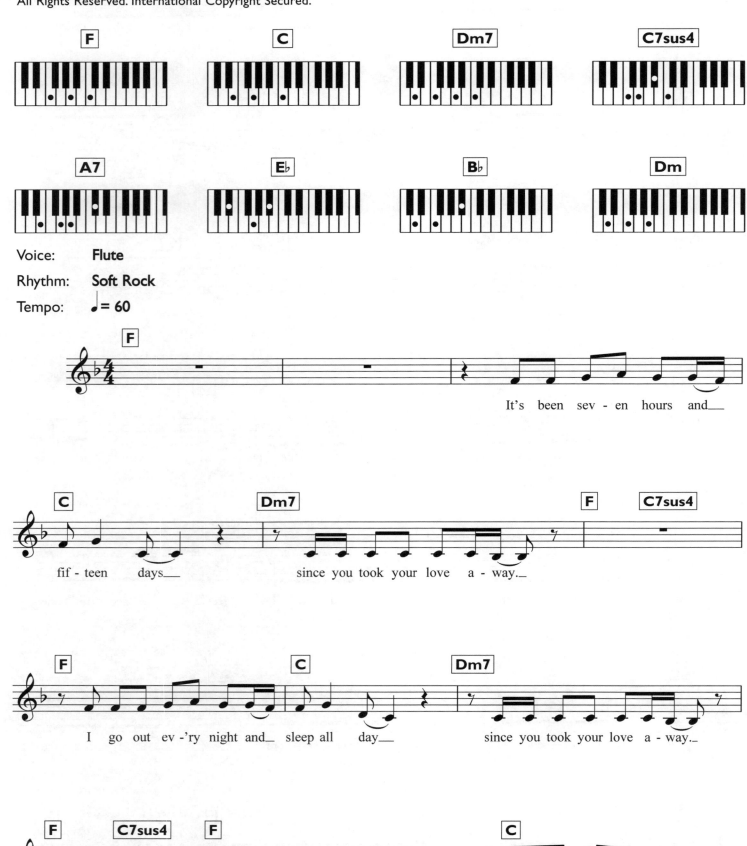

Voice: **Flute**

Rhythm: **Soft Rock**

Tempo: ♩ = 60

It's been sev - en hours and___ fif - teen days___ since you took your love a - way.___

I go out ev -'ry night and___ sleep all day___ since you took your love a - way.___

Since you been gone I can do what - ev - er I want._____

(SITTIN' ON) THE DOCK OF THE BAY

Words & Music by Steve Cropper & Otis Redding

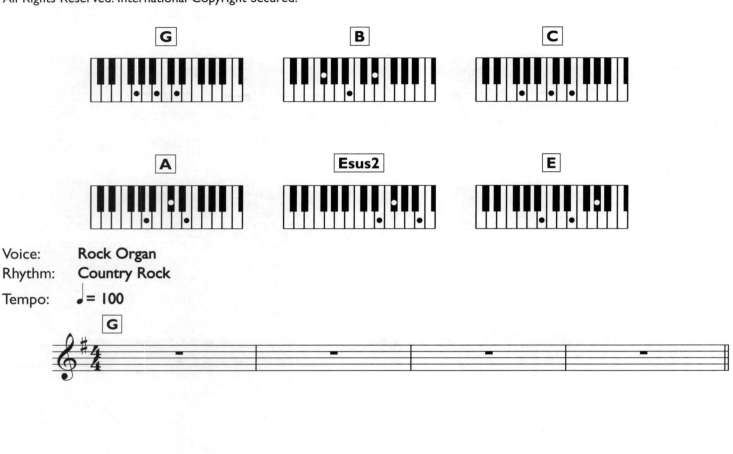

Voice: **Rock Organ**
Rhythm: **Country Rock**
Tempo: ♩ = 100

Sit-tin' in the morn-in' sun,___ I'll be sit-tin' when the eve-nin' come.___

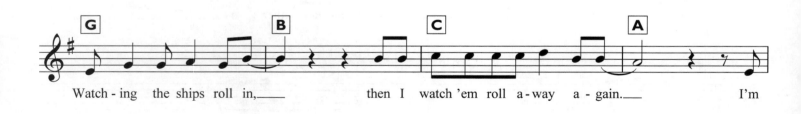

Watch-ing the ships roll in,___ then I watch 'em roll a-way a-gain.___ I'm

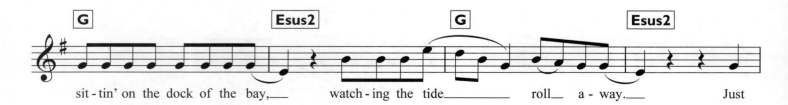

sit-tin' on the dock of the bay,___ watch-ing the tide___ roll___ a-way.___ Just

SUSPICIOUS MINDS

Words & Music by Francis Zambon

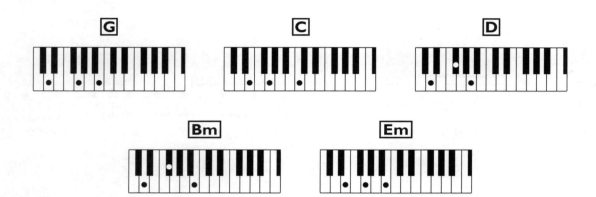

Voice: **Alto Saxophone**

Rhythm: **Love Ballad**

Tempo: ♩ = **100**

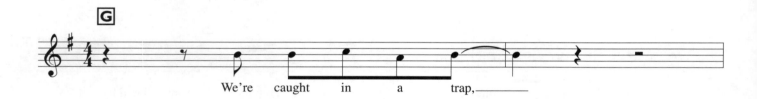

We're caught in a trap,_____

I can't walk out,_____

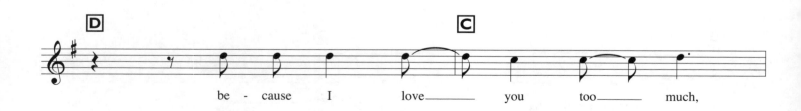

be - cause I love_____ you too_____ much,

ba - - - by._____

SWEET CAROLINE

Words & Music by Neil Diamond

Voice: **Trumpet**

Rhythm: **Lite Pop**

Tempo: ♩. = **128**

TAINTED LOVE

Words & Music by Ed Cobb
© Copyright 1967 Equinox Music.
Campbell Connelly & Company Limited.

Repeat ad lib. to fade

WATERLOO

Words & Music by Benny Andersson, Stig Anderson & Björn Ulvaeus

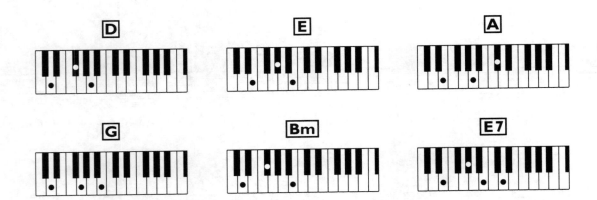

Voice: **Voice Ooh**

Rhythm: **Slow Rock 1**

Tempo: ♩ = 130

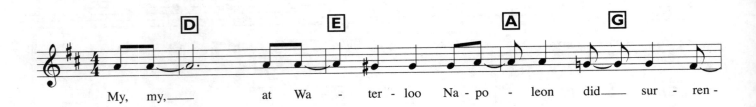

My, my,____ at Wa - ter - loo Na - po - leon did sur - ren-

-der._____ Oh, yeah,____ and I____ have met my des-

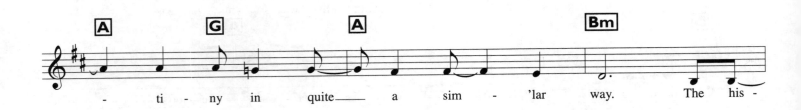

-ti - ny in quite____ a sim - 'lar way. The his-

-to - ry book____ on the shelf____ is al - ways re - peat - ing it - self.____

Wa - ter - loo, I___ was de - feat - ed, you won___

___ the war. Wa - ter - loo, pro -

- mise to love___ you for - ev - er more. Wa -

- ter - loo, could - n't es - cape___ if I want - ed to. Wa -

- ter - loo, know - ing my fate___ is to be___

___ with you. Wa - wa - wa - wa - wa - ter - loo. Fin -

Repeat to fade

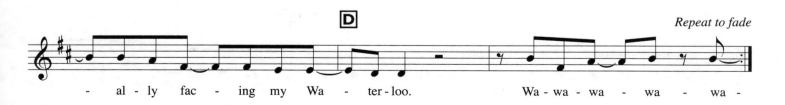

- al - ly fac - ing my Wa - ter - loo. Wa - wa - wa - wa - wa -

YOU'RE THE ONE THAT I WANT

Words & Music by John Farrar

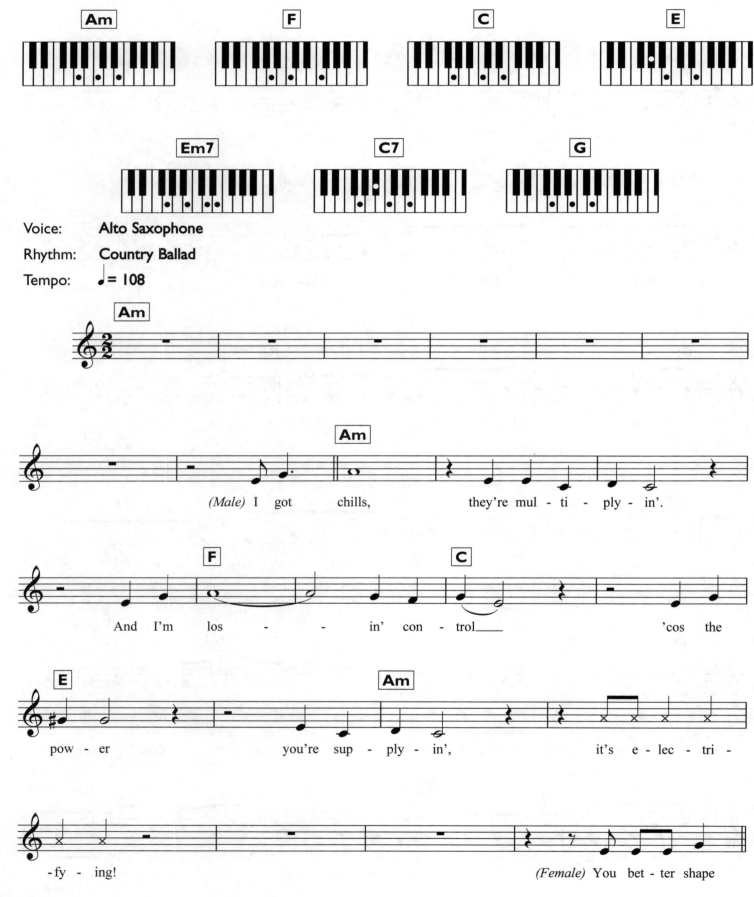

EASIEST KEYBOARD COLLECTION

Easy-to-play melody line arrangements for all keyboards with chord symbols and lyrics. Suggested registration, rhythm and tempo are included for each song together with keyboard diagrams showing left-hand chord voicings used.

 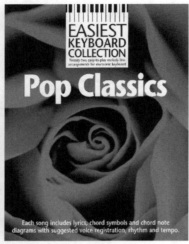  

Showstoppers

Consider Yourself (Oliver!), Do You Hear The People Sing? (Les Misérables), I Know Him So Well (Chess), Maria (West Side Story), Smoke Gets In Your Eyes (Roberta) and 17 more big stage hits.
Order No. AM944218

Pop Classics

A Whiter Shade Of Pale (Procol Harum), Bridge Over Troubled Water (Simon & Garfunkel), Crocodile Rock (Elton John) and 19 more classic hit songs, including Hey Jude (The Beatles), Imagine (John Lennon), and Massachusetts (The Bee Gees).
Order No. AM944196

90s Hits

Over 20 of the greatest hits of the 1990s, including Always (Bon Jovi), Fields Of Gold (Sting), Have I Told You Lately (Rod Stewart), One Sweet Day (Mariah Carey), Say You'll Be There (Spice Girls), and Wonderwall (Oasis).
Order No. AM944229

Abba

A great collection of 22 Abba hit songs. Includes: Dancing Queen, Fernando, I Have A Dream, Mamma Mia, Super Trouper, Take A Chance On Me, Thank You For The Music, The Winner Takes It All, and Waterloo.
Order No. AM959860

Also available...

Ballads, Order No. AM952116   **The Corrs**, Order No. AM959849

The Beatles, Order No. NO90686   **Elton John**, Order No. AM958320

Boyzone, Order No. AM958331   **Film Themes**, Order No. AM952050

Broadway, Order No. AM952127   **Hits of the 90s,** Order No. AM955780

Celine Dion, Order No. AM959850   **Jazz Classics**, Order No. AM952061

Chart Hits, Order No. AM952083   **Love Songs**, Order No. AM950708

Christmas, Order No. AM952105   **Pop Hits**, Order No. AM952072

Classic Blues, Order No. AM950697   **60s Hits**, Order No. AM955768

Classics, Order No. AM952094   **80s Hits**, Order No. AM955779

...plus many more!